Mighty Mighty MONSTERS

THE WOLF BOY'S WISH

www.raintreepublishers.co.uk
Visit our website to find out
more information about
Raintree books.

To order:
☎ Phone 0845 6044371
🖹 Fax +44 (0) 1865 312263
✉ Email myorders@raintreepublishers.co.uk

Customers from outside the UK please telephone +44 1865 312262

Raintree is an imprint of Capstone Global Library Limited,
a company incorporated in England and Wales having its registered
office at 7 Pilgrim Street, London, EC4V 6LB
– Registered company number: 6695582

First published by Stone Arch Books in 2010
First published in the United Kingdom in paperback in 2012
The moral rights of the proprietor have been asserted.

Edited by Siân Smith
Originated by Capstone Global Library Ltd
Printed and bound in China by South China Printing Company

ISBN 978 1 406 24231 7 (paperback)
16 15 14 13 12
10 9 8 7 6 5 4 3 2 1

British Library Cataloguing in Publication Data
O'Reilly, Sean, 1974
741.5-dc23
A full catalogue record for this book is available
from the British Library

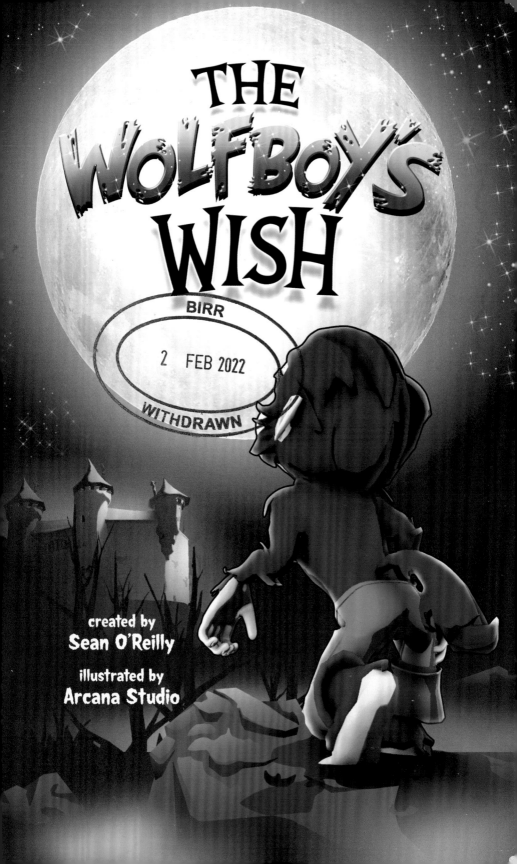

THE WOLFBOY'S WISH

created by
Sean O'Reilly

illustrated by
Arcana Studio

In a strange corner of the world known as Transylmania . . .

Legendary monsters were born.

WELCOME TO TRANSYLMANIA

But long before their frightful fame, these classic creatures faced fears of their own.

To take on terrifying teachers and homework horrors,
they formed the most fearsome friendship on Earth . . .

MEET THE MONSTERS!

CLAUDE
The Invisible Boy

FRANKIE
Frankenstein

MARY
Future bride of
Frankenstein

POTO
The Phantom
of the Opera

MILTON
The Grim Reaper

It was an extra exciting day at Transylmania School...

RRRRIIIIINNGGG!!

To whoever finds this map, I say thee welcome to it. Its mysteries are yours to unfold, and the prize within yours to do with as you will. Spend wisely what you find there.

Know this: Any attempt you make to reach this treasure, you must make alone. Tempt not others with your quest. Its prize is meant only for you.

Good luck!

Silas V. Suvious

Shouldn't you be at summer school?
Who has time for summer school when there are treasures to hunt?
Yeah, but Talbot, it's school. You have to go.
But this is an adventure we can't pass up.
See that? That's a lamp!
The kind with a genie inside!
If I get that lamp, I can wish for anything I want—
Talbot, the map clearly states you are to pursue this quest by yourself.

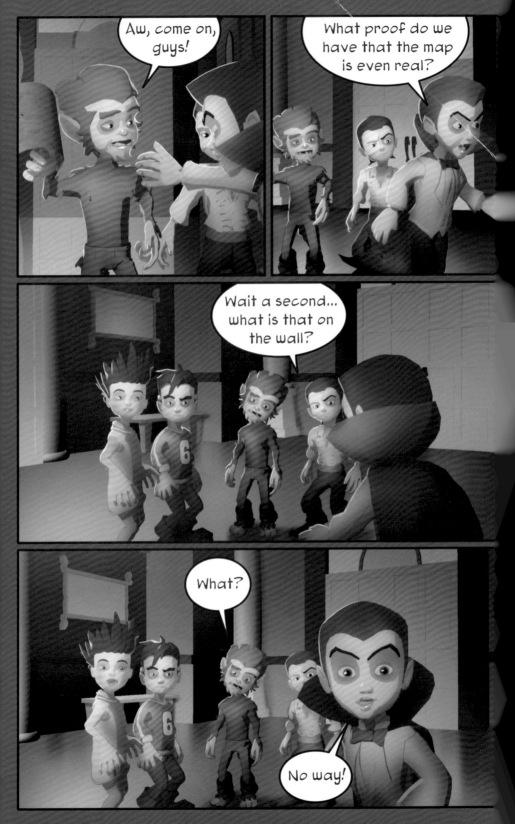

23

That's a portrait of Silas V. Suvious. The founder of Transylmania!

So what?

Legend has it that Suvious landed on the shores of what would become our great home...

and less than a month later, the entire town was built... like magic...

So we'll be going, then?

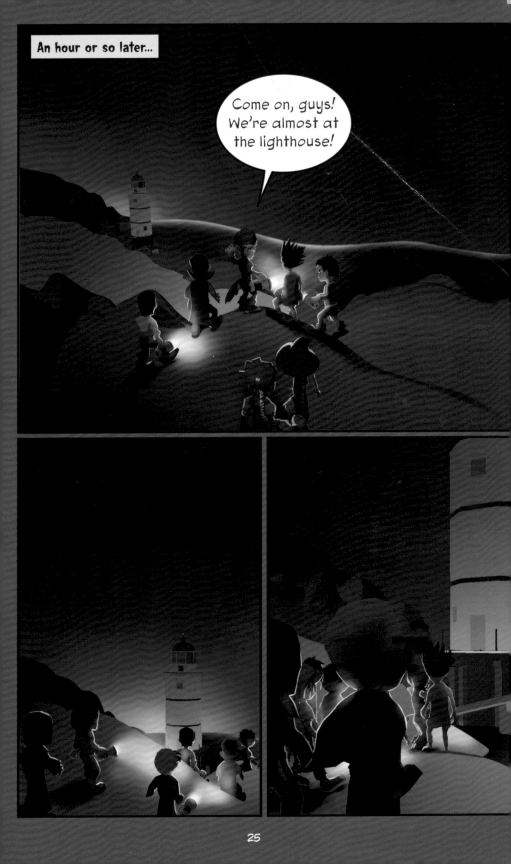

According to the map, the cave entrance is directly west of here.
Then what are we waiting for?
Does this seem a little too easy?
It's almost like Suvious wants us to find it.

The lamp! I just have to have the lamp!

I don't want to be a screw-up any more.

What are you talking about?

I'm the only one who ended up in summer school.

The important thing is to try again, you know?

I know. But it's hard.

Plus, with one wish, I won't have summer school.

Yeah, but Talbot, there won't always be a magic lamp to wish away your problems.

Can't we at least try? I mean, we've come all this way.

Okay. It's worth a shot.

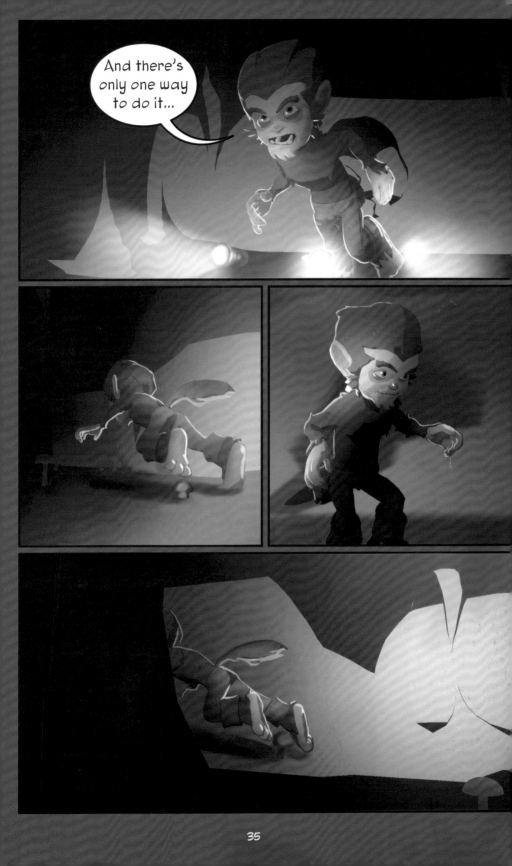

Tsk tsk tsk. You were told to come alone.
I am authorized to penalize you one of three wishes for disobeying the rules. Next!
Ugh! Okay.
I... I wish again that you rescue my friends.
Tsk tsk tsk. Oh, this will never do.
I am authorized to penalize you one of two wishes for wishing for the same thing twice.

What would you have wished for originally?

...help with my homework...

Oh, that never gets old!

I am authorized to penalize you one wish for asking for something you could do yourself.

Oh no.

I said authorized, not obligated. You get a reprieve.

You have one wish left. Remember the rules this time.

I wish I never found that stupid map in the first place!

Now that's more like it!

THE MAGIC OF
GENIES

- Stories featuring genies have been around for hundreds of years, including the popular Arabian Nights tale *The Fisherman and the Genie*.

- In Rudyard Kipling's famous story *How the Camel Got His Hump*, a Genie (or Djinn) plays a starring roll. The "Djinn in Charge of All Deserts" is the one who gives the lazy camel his hump.

- In 1965, a popular TV show called *I Dream of Jeannie* began. It featured a pretty blonde genie who was completely in love with her master. It ran for five seasons. Today, shows like *Fairly Odd Parents* and *Wizards of Waverly Place* feature genies and their magical powers.

- In the tale *Aladdin and his Magic Lamp*, the genie grants his master unlimited wishes. In 1992, it became a huge hit movie for Disney under the title of *Aladdin*.

- Famous basketball player Shaquille O'Neal starred as a genie in the 1996 film *Kazaam*. Unlike most genies, he lived in a boombox instead of a magic lamp or bottle.

GLOSSARY

authorized given official permission for something to happen

disobeying going against the rules or someone's wishes

irresponsible reckless and lacking a sense of responsiblility

obligated made someone do something because of a law, promise, contract, or sense of duty

penalize to make someone suffer a penalty or punishment for something the person has done wrong

pursue to continue something

quest a long search

reprieve to cancel or delay a punishment

unacceptable not good enough to be allowed or accepted

DISCUSSION QUESTIONS

1. Because Talbot didn't finish his schoolwork, he had to go to summer school. Do you think that was a fair punishment? Why or why not?

2. Do you think Talbot showed he was responsible by the end of the story? Explain.

3. Were you surprised by the end of the story? Why or why not?

WRITING PROMPTS

1. Make a list of three things you would wish for if you found a magic lamp.

2. If you found a treasure map, what kind of treasure would you want to find? Write a paragraph describing it.

3. How would you feel if you had to go to summer school? Write a paragraph explaining your feelings.

Information books

The Mystery of Vampires and Werewolves
   (Can Science Solve?), Chris Oxlade (Heinemann
   Library, 2008)

Vampires and the Undead (Dark Side), Anita Ganeri
   (Wayland, 2010)

Graphic novels

Dracula (Graphic Revolve), Bram Stoker, retold by
   Michael Burgan (Raintree, 2009)

Frankenstein (Graphic Revolve), Mary Shelley, retold
   by Michael Burgan (Raintree, 2009)

The Invisible Man, (Graphic Chillers), H. G. Wells,
   retold by Joeming Dunn (Franklin Watts, 2010)

Website

learnenglishkids.britishcouncil.org/en/make-
   your-own/make-your-monster
Visit this website to create your own monster. You
can also invent your own scary story, dangerous
animal, or superhero.

Mighty Mighty MONSTERS ADVENTURES

Hide and Shriek!
ISBN: 978 1 406 23718 4

Lost in Spooky Forest
ISBN: 978 1 406 23720 7

The King of Halloween Castle
ISBN: 978 1 406 23719 1

New Monster in School
ISBN: 978 1 406 23723 8

Monster Mansion
ISBN: 978 1 406 23721 4

My Missing Monster
ISBN: 978 1 406 23722 1

Monster Beach
ISBN: 978 1 406 24226 3

The Missing Mummy
ISBN: 978 1 406 24227 0

The Monster Crooks
ISBN: 978 1 406 24228 7

The Toy Snatcher
ISBN: 978 1 406 24230 0

The Wolfboy's Wish
ISBN: 978 1 406 24231 7

The Scare Fair
ISBN: 978 1 406 24229 4

They're Fang-tastic!

ABOUT
SEAN O'REILLY
AND ARCANA STUDIO

As a lifelong comics fan, Sean O'Reilly dreamed of becoming a comic book creator. In 2004, he realized that dream by creating Arcana Studio. In one short year, O'Reilly took his studio from a one-person operation in his house to an award-winning comic book publisher with more than 150 graphic novels produced for Harper Collins, Simon & Schuster, Random House, Scholastic, and others.

Within a year, the company won many awards including the Shuster Award for Outstanding Publisher and the Moonbeam Award for top children's graphic novel. O'Reilly also won the Top 40 Under 40 award from the city of Vancouver and authored *The Clockwork Girl* for Top Graphic Novel at Book Expo America in 2009.

Currently, O'Reilly is one of the most prolific independent comic book writers in Canada. While showing no signs of slowing down in comics, he now also writes screenplays and adapts his creations for the big screen.